Looking It Up
Learning Library Skills

by Mary Preston Foster

Fearon Teacher Aids
a division of
David S. Lake Publishers
Belmont, California

Illustrator: Marilynn Barr
Designer: Irene Imfeld

ISBN 0-8224-4345-7

Printed in the United States of America

1. 9 8 7 6 5 4 3 2 1

Contents

Introduction

The first step I took toward writing this book was to decide that it was my responsibility to teach students reference skills. I wanted them to be able to use the card catalog, understand the library's organization, and know how to use reference books. To do this, I developed reference skills worksheets, lessons, games, and tests. It worked. The students I taught earned high scores on the national standardized tests that cover reference skills.

I thank you for buying this book. Please make it earn its price. Use it. Get angry because I make it all sound so simple. I really know it's not. I know that when you get to the part about Indians, every child in the class will have to tell you everything he or she knows about Indians. I know that one will jump in while everybody else is talking and tell you that his dog had puppies. Persevere! Most of all, make this book work for you. Use it as a guide to teaching reference skills, but present the information in your own words.

My thanks to my children, Susan, Anson, and Tommy; and also to Jean Murray, Peggy Hanna, Anne Oplinger, and Sandra Whiteside.

Unit I • Call Numbers

The objective of this unit is to help students become familiar with call numbers: where they are found, how they are made, and how they are used.

Lesson 1 • The Two Lines of a Call Number

Make an overhead transparency that shows the abbreviations for the different types of books found in your library: *R* for reference books, *B* for biography, and so on. Put the transparency on the overhead projector and explain what each of the abbreviations stands for.

When the students understand the abbreviations, tell them that a *call number* identifies where a book can be found in the library. The call number can be compared to the address number on a house because it tells the book's address in the library. Each call number consists of two parts; the top part indicates the section of the library and the bottom part consists of the first initial of the author's last name.

Before you continue, tell the students that books about facts, non-fiction books, are arranged according to a number system they will learn later. Reference books, the nonfiction books that can't be checked out of the library, are also arranged according to that number system (the Dewey Decimal System).

Go over all the places where call numbers appear—the spine of the book, the card in the card catalog, the book pocket, and the card inside the book. Discuss why the call number appears in each of these places.

Lesson 2 • Identifying Call Numbers

Briefly review the two parts of the call number and the various sections of the library. Be sure the students understand how the two parts of the call number are different, and then hand out the "Call Number Clues" worksheet (page 18). You may wish to do this worksheet with the class as a whole. Tell the students that you will be giving them a call numbers test in a few days and ask them to take the worksheet home to study.

Lesson 3 • Call Numbers Game

Use the "Questions for the Call Numbers Game" (page 19) for one of the three games below.

Game 1

Divide the students into small groups. Duplicate one game board (page 20) for each group. Get a pack of 3" × 5" index cards and write one of the "Questions for the Call Numbers Game" on the front of each one. On the back of each card, write the answer to the question (see the "Answer Key" on page 57 if necessary). For each game, provide dice or a spinner. Give each student a token to move around the board.

Each student spins the spinner or rolls the dice and then draws a question card from the top of the pile. (The question cards must have their answer sides face down.) If the student answers the question correctly, he or she gets to move the appropriate number of spaces around the board. If the student fails to answer the question correctly, the next student takes a turn. The student who reaches the end of the board first wins the game.

Game 2

Make a copy of the "Call Numbers Game Sheet" (page 21) for each student in the class. Give each student a paper clip. Read the "Questions for the Call Numbers Game" to the students and have them answer each question by placing the paper clip on the correct answer on the game sheet. Quickly check each student's answer and provide a small reward for each correct answer.

Game 3

Divide the students into two teams and ask them all to stand in a line with their respective teams. Ask the first student on one team the first of the "Questions for the Call Numbers Game." If the student answers correctly, he or she remains standing. If the student misses the question, he or she must sit down. Repeat this procedure with the first student on the other team. Give each student a turn. Play until one team is sitting down or until you run out of time. The team with the most people standing wins the game.

Lesson 4 • Call Numbers Test

Give each student a copy of the "Call Numbers Test" (pages 22–23). Go around the room and correct the test as the students finish and raise their hands. Use a "Super" stamp or give out colorful stickers for good work.

Unit II • Library Organization

The objective of this unit is to teach students how the library is organized and to help them understand the types of materials available in each section of the library.

Lesson 1 • The Library Map

Use the "Library Map Outline" (page 24) to create a map of your library. Duplicate several copies of the "Library Map Outline" and cut out the bookshelf strips. Use the rectangle to represent the walls of the library. (You may need to alter the outline if your library is not in a single, rectangular room.)

Draw lightly in pencil the placement of all the bookshelves in the library and then glue the bookshelf strips over these marks. Next, draw in your checkout desk, your card catalog, and any other elements in the room. Indicate where the door is, and mark it with a *D. Don't* label these sections on this sheet.

Make a transparency of the library map for the overhead projector. (At the same time, duplicate one copy of the map for each student and set the copies aside for Lesson 3.)

Take another sheet of overhead projection film and lay it on top of the library map. On the overlay, write in the sections of the library: fiction, reference, nonfiction, and so on. When the students are ready for the lesson, put the library map on the overhead projector. Show them where the door is and then move to the areas on the map that are easiest to understand. Discuss each section of the map and the types of books found there. Then place the overlay on the map. Go over the library map again and ask students to identify the type of books in each location.

Spend the rest of the class period reading to the students or letting them read books of their choice. It's important to encourage them to think of the library as a friendly and comfortable place to be.

Lesson 2 • The Arrangement of the Books

Make an overlay that can be placed over the library map transparency and that shows a sample call number for each section.

Put the library map on the overhead projector and review the sections of the library with the students. Next, place the overlay on the overhead projector and discuss each sample call number.

When the students have answered their questions about call numbers, take them on a tour of the library. Point out each section and show them the call numbers on the books. Point out shelves and books that might interest them.

After the tour, return to the overhead projector and remove the overlay. Let some of the students come to the overhead projector and identify the sections of the library. Answer any questions they may have about the sections.

Lesson 3 • Library Map Game

Briefly review the library map on the overhead projector, as well as both the overlays. Using the "Questions for the Library Map Game" (page 25), play the game described below.

Give each student a copy of the outline map. Tell the class not to mark on the maps because they will be used for the library map test later. Give each student a marker (a paper clip, button, or penny) and explain that you will read aloud some questions about the library's organization. In response to each question, the students should place their markers in the appropriate place on the library map. Either go around the room and check each answer yourself or assign this task to another person. Give a small reward for correct answers.

One alternative to this game is to divide the class into two teams and have each team member answer a question by pointing to the correct answer on the overhead projection of the library map. The team scores one point for each correct answer.

Lesson 4 • Library Map Test

Give each student a copy of the library map, unlabeled. Put the names of the sections you want them to label on the board or on the overhead projector. When they are finished labeling the map, have them raise their hands so you can correct their work. Give good hints to students who are having trouble, and let the students take the completed maps home to study and keep for reference.

To encourage the students along, you may wish to give the "Super Student Award" (page 26) for good work.

Unit III • Parts of a Book

The objective of this unit is to make students familiar with all of the parts of a book and to help them understand where each part is located and how each part is used.

Lesson 1 • The Front of a Book

Give each student a book to look at as you present this lesson. Large, colorful reference books are a good choice. After you have given the students a minute or two to look at their books, introduce them to each part of the front of the book by asking appropriate questions.

The Cover
What kinds of covers are on the books? Why are some of the covers plain and others illustrated? What information is on the cover?

The Spine
What is written on the spine of the book? Why is it important to have a call number on the spine?

The Title Page
What information do you find on the title page of the book? (Show the students that the first page of the book may be a blank page called the flyleaf. Be sure that the students understand that the title is the name of the book, the author is the person who wrote the book, the illustrator is the person who drew the pictures, and the publisher is the company that issued the book.

The Acknowledgments Page
If any of the students have a book with an acknowledgments page, explain that this page allows the author to thank the people who made the book possible, or to express appreciation.

The Preface, Foreword, or Introduction
Explain that the *foreword* is usually a statement by someone other than the author and it may serve as an introduction to the book's topic.

A *preface* is usually written by the author, and it usually describes why the book was written. An introduction may give background information about the book's subject and lead into the main part of the book.

Lesson 2 • The Table of Contents and the Index

Choose a book with a clear table of contents and an index to show the students. Discuss the purpose of each of these parts and make sure the students understand the differences between them.

Using the book you have chosen, ask the students specific questions about where they might find certain subjects by using the table of contents or the index.

When students understand how to use the table of contents and the index, hand out the two worksheets. "Using the Index" (page 27) and "Using the Table of Contents" (page 28). Go over these worksheets with the students and answer any questions they may have.

Lesson 3 • The Glossary, Bibliography, and Appendix

Again, give each student a book to examine during this lesson. Try to provide books that have a glossary, a bibliography, and an appendix.

The Glossary
Ask the students to find the glossary in the books you have provided. Explain how the glossary can be used as a dictionary for the words in the book.

The Bibliography
Have the students find the bibliography in their books. Tell them that it may also have a title such as "Suggested Reading" and that it lists books and articles related to the book's subject.

The Appendix
The appendix of the book contains supplementary information that is not in the main part of the book. It may include graphs, tables, or illustrative material. Ask students to describe the appendices in their books.

Lesson 4 • Parts-of-a-Book Crossword Puzzle

Review all the parts of a book with the students and hand out the crossword puzzle (page 29). You may have to help them get started on the puzzle if they are not familiar with the crossword puzzle format. The puzzle takes the place of a test on this unit.

Unit IV • Alphabetizing

The objective of this unit is to teach students how to use alphabetical order to find books on the shelves and to find words in a dictionary, an encyclopedia, and a card catalog.

Lesson 1 • Finding Words in the Dictionary

Give each student a dictionary for this lesson. Explain how alphabetizing is a universal system for organizing information, and ask students to name things that are alphabetized (telephone books, files, dictionaries, and so on).

Ask the students to open their dictionaries to any page. Point out the words at the top of the page and ask the students what those words are. When the students have figured out that these words, the *guide words*, are the first and last words on the page, show them how to find a specific word by using the guide words. After looking up a few words with the students, hand out the "Gliding Through Guide Words" worksheet (page 30).

Lesson 2 • Finding Words in the Encyclopedia

Before class, obtain one volume of an encyclopedia for each student. Attach an index card to the outside of each volume and write two or three words on the card that can be found in the volume. Give each student a volume with a card attached.

Discuss how a dictionary differs from an encyclopedia. Help the students understand that an encyclopedia gives *detailed* information about subjects. Ask students to look up the words that are on the cards and jot down some interesting facts about those subjects. When each student has found at least one of the words, ask them to describe what they learned. Hand out the "Alphabet Scramble" worksheet (page 31).

Lesson 3 • Finding Words in the Card Catalog

Before class, attach an index card to a card catalog drawer for each student. On each index card, write two or three words that can be found on cards in that particular drawer. Give each student a drawer with a card attached. Show them how to use the guide words written on the card catalog's tabs to find cards in the drawer quickly.

Ask the students to locate the words on their cards in the card catalog by using the guide words. As the students are working, check to make sure each one understands how to find the words.

Lesson 4 • Finding Books on the Shelves

Before class, take a number of index cards and write the title and author of a *fiction book* on each one. Make sure each of these books is in the library before you start the lesson.

Show the students how the labels on the bookshelves serve as guide words for finding books. Explain the labeling system in your library. (Remember, the Dewey Decimal System will be introduced in Unit V.) When all the students' questions have been answered, play the game described below.

The "Find That Book" Game

Divide the class into two teams. Give a *different* title-and-author index card to one student from each team. (Fights may break out if you give students the same book to look up.) The first student to find his or her book scores a point for the team. Tell the students whether they may coach their team members during the search. Coaching allows everyone to become involved in the game.

Be sure to allot enough time so that every student has an opportunity to find a book. The team that scores the most points by the end of the game wins.

Unit V • The Dewey Decimal System

The objective of this unit is to teach students the Dewey Decimal System used on nonfiction books and to help them learn to find books in the non-fiction section of the library.

Lesson 1 • Introducing the Dewey Decimal System

Begin this unit with a "hero" story about Melvil Dewey, the man who came up with the Dewey Decimal library classification system: "Once upon a time there was a young man named Melvil Dewey. . . ." Make up a simple story that tells how Melvil Dewey got tired of trying to find books on a particular subject by remembering who wrote the books. All the books were arranged in alphabetical order by the authors' last names. To change this system, Melvil Dewey developed a way to organize books by subject rather than by author. The system he came up with a hundred years ago is still used by most libraries today.

Make a transparency of the "Dewey Decimal System" (page 32) and place it on the overhead projector. Explain to the students that the Dewey Decimal System classifies books by dividing them into ten main groups, each represented by a group of numbers. Each of these divisions is further subdivided. To find books in the nonfiction section, students don't have to memorize the categories, but they do need to understand how the system works. Go over each category in the system and give some examples of the subdivisions. For example, the numbers 630–639 represent Agriculture, which includes Garden Crops, Field Crops, and other subdivisions. Give the students enough time to become familiar with the different divisions of the Dewey Decimal System, and be sure to explain words they may not be familiar with, such as "Technology" or "Philosophy."

Hand out the "Melvil Who?" worksheet (page 33).

Lesson 2 • Becoming Familiar with the Dewey Decimal System

Put the "Dewey Decimal System" transparency on the overhead projector again and review the different categories with the students. Point out some of the unusual aspects about the categories. For example, although they are fictional, fairy tales can be found in the 398 section of the nonfiction books.

Tell the students that all books with the same call number are further classified alphabetically by the authors' last names. If one author has written several books on the same topic, the books are arranged alphabetically by title.

Hand out the "What's the Number?" worksheet (pages 34–35) and do it with the class.

Lesson 3 • Creating the Dewey Decimal Mural

This lesson requires more preparation than any of the others, but it is fun and well worth your effort. To prepare for class, follow the procedure below:

1. Cut out as many pictures as you can find from all kinds of magazines. You may want to ask the students to bring in pictures from magazines as well. Make sure that you can *clearly* classify the subjects of the pictures in one of the Dewey Decimal categories. Discard the pictures that are not easy to place in the categories. Look for bright, colorful pictures in all shapes and sizes. The more pictures you have, the better your final product will be. Weed out the dull and vague.

2. Cut strips of paper to make the labels for the mural. Write the key words from each of the Dewey Decimal categories on the strips of paper.

3. Unroll a sheet of butcher paper in front of each set of book-shelves to find the length of the mural pieces. Draw a double line down the butcher paper for each section of shelves. Draw a single line down the butcher paper to mark each Dewey Decimal number category. Write in the correct Dewey Decimal numbers for each division on the paper. For example:

SECTION 1   SECTION 2

000	100	200	300	400	500	600	700

4. Label the sections with the key words of the Dewey Decimal System (the paper strips cut out in step 2).

When the students come in, place the "Dewey Decimal System" transparency on the overhead projector. Have the pictures on a table nearby and the butcher paper on the floor in front of the appropriate bookshelves. Ask the students to form a line. Their job will be to file past the table, pick up a picture, come to the overhead projector, and correctly identify the category of the Dewey Decimal System that the picture represents. Stand at the projector with a jar of rubber cement and put some on the back of each student's picture as he or she correctly identifies the category. Have the students go to the mural and place their pictures in the correct places. Let them repeat this process until the mural is complete. Don't worry about misplaced pictures. The rubber cement will enable you to move misplaced pictures without damaging the background.

When the mural is complete, laminate it and put it up over the appropriate shelves so that the students can use it as a reference when they are looking for books.

Lesson 4 • Finding Nonfiction Books

For this lesson, play the "Find That Book" game described on page 8, but have the students look for nonfiction books. Again, be sure that the books you write down on the index cards are in the library when the students are ready to play the game. Before you start the game, show the students how to use the guide labels on the bookshelves in the nonfiction section. Encourage them to refer to the mural's pictures to help locate the proper shelves.

Unit VI • The Card Catalog

The objective of this unit is to help students learn how to use the card catalog and understand the difference between title, author, and subject cards.

Lesson 1 • Introducing the Card Catalog

Make a transparency for the overhead projector of a picture of the card catalog. Make another transparency of three cards: a subject card, an author card, and a title card.

Begin this lesson with the picture of the card catalog on the overhead projector. Remind the students that they already know how to find cards in alphabetical order. This lesson will focus on the different kinds of cards in the card catalog.

Compare the card catalog to a department store catalog and explain that the card catalog serves the same function for the library that the store catalog does for the store. The card catalog gives a handy list of all the things that are in the library, just as the store catalog lets a person look up an item without having to walk all over the store. Tell the students that as new books are received and old books are replaced, the library adds and deletes catalog cards.

Ask the students if they have ever used a store catalog. Point out that when they look at the different pictures in the catalog to decide what they want, they are shopping by *subject*. Explain that the card catalog can be used in much the same way. If students are interested in a specific subject, they can look it up in the card catalog by subject. Cards arranged by subject in the card catalog are called *subject cards*. If students want to read a book by a particular author but don't know the book's title, they can look up the book by using an *author card*. These cards are arranged alphabetically by the author's last name. Books are also arranged by title on *title cards* so that people don't have to know the author of a book to find it in the catalog.

Put the transparency of the three catalog cards on the overhead projector. Discuss the difference between the cards and remind the students that all the cards will be in alphabetical order by the first word on the card. Explain that book titles beginning with *A, The,* and *An* are alphabetized according to the next word in the title. Abbreviations such as *Dr.* and *St.* are alphabetized as if they were spelled out. Names beginning with *Mc* are alphabetized as *Mac.*

Lesson 2 • Recognizing Information on Catalog Cards

To help students recognize the information given on a catalog card, hand out the three "Cat on a Log" worksheets (pages 36–38). Do these three worksheets with the students. At some point, the students will realize that the information on the three cards is the same. When they discover this, remind them that the information about the book is merely rearranged on each card.

Lesson 3 • Finding the Books

This is the lesson that all the previous lessons have been leading up to. Give each student a card catalog drawer to which you have attached an index card. Each index card should list a title, author, and subject. The student's task is to find a catalog card that has that title, author, and subject, and then to locate the book on the shelf.

Have the students raise their hands when they find the appropriate card. Check to make sure that the cards are correct, and give each student a piece of scratch paper to write down the book's call number. Ask the students if they know the section of the library to look in, and then send them on their way.

Make sure that all the books you ask the students to look up are on the shelves before class begins. At the end of the class, encourage the students to go down to a county or city library to show off their new book-finding skills.

Lesson 4 • Practicing Card Catalog Skills

Give each student a copy of the "Who Are You?" and "What Am I?" worksheet puzzles (pages 39–40). Go over the directions on each of the worksheets and briefly remind students how to look up cards in the catalog. You may want to have students do these worksheets during an independent work time to avoid having all the students crowding around the catalog at one time.

Tell the class that each person who completes the worksheets correctly will receive a small reward. Be sure to look over the worksheets in advance to make sure that the card catalog contains all the books. If you are missing any of the books, substitute other titles or authors that fit the puzzle.

Unit VII • The Encyclopedia

The objective of this unit is to teach students how to use an encyclopedia, including the index, the outlines, and the "See also" references at the end of articles. Students will also learn to paraphrase information and use the large headings in encyclopedia articles.

Lesson 1 • Introducing the Encyclopedia

Give each student an encyclopedia volume along with an index card that lists two articles in that volume. Choose one long article and one short article, and try to find articles that will interest the students.

Discuss copyright laws and plagiarism with the students. Be sure they understand that it is illegal to copy something word for word and present it as original work. For this reason, it's important for them to learn to put things into their own words. Remind them that they do this all the time. When someone asks them what a book or movie was about, they respond in their own words. Tell the students that to *paraphrase* is to express the meaning of something *in one's own words*.

Have the students find the two articles on the index card and read the shorter of the two articles carefully. Help them find the articles if necessary. When they are finished reading, ask them to close the encyclopedias and put the index card at the front of the volume. Go around the room and let each student tell the class what his or her article was about.

Hand out the "So Many Ways to Paraphrase!" worksheet (page 41) and tell the students to use their encyclopedia volumes to complete it.

Lesson 2 • Finding Information in the Encyclopedia

Give each student an encyclopedia volume along with an index card that lists two articles in that volume. (Use the same index cards you prepared for Lesson 1.) This lesson will focus on the longer encyclopedia article. The purpose of the lesson is to help students become familiar with the different parts of a long encyclopedia article.

Have the students find the long article given on their index cards. Ask them to write down the *large headings* in the article to get a sense of the whole article. As they are writing, go around the room and ask them specific questions about their articles. Examples: Which section of this article would you read if you wanted to know who the first governor of Connecticut was? Which section of the article on dogs would you read if you wanted to know what to feed a puppy?

Be sure that the students look at all of the maps, graphs, and charts in their articles. Ask them about the information contained in these figures. Examples: When might you use the maps, graphs, and charts? What kinds of information do they provide?

When you have talked with each student, have everyone stop copying the headings and turn to the end of the articles. Point out the *outline* at the end of an article and tell the students that it *is* acceptable to use the outline to help them organize papers for school.

Ask the students to look at the *bibliography* at the end of the article to find other books on the same subject. If any of the articles have a "See also" reference for *related articles*, explain that this is another possible source of information. Finally, remind the students that when they are looking up information in the encyclopedia, they need to know what the *key words* of their subject are. Hand out the "Encyclopedia Wizard" worksheet (page 42) to give the students practice in selecting key words.

Lesson 3 • Using the Index

Remind students how they have used the index in a book to look up specific information quickly. The encyclopedia's index serves the same function; it lists the volume and page number of specific topics and is arranged alphabetically by topic.

Ask the students to suggest some topics they are interested in. Demonstrate how to look the topics up in the encyclopedia. Then have three or four students look up a few topics suggested by classmates.

When the students understand how to use the index, hand out the "Index Clues" worksheet (page 43).

Lesson 4 • Encyclopedia Test

Give each student an encyclopedia volume along with an index card that lists an article in the volume and one question answered in that article. After handing out the "Encyclopedia Test" (pages 44-45), tell the students to answer Part II of the test by using the encyclopedia volumes they have been given.

Unit VIII • Other Reference Books

The objective of this unit is to teach the students how and when to use a dictionary, an atlas, and an almanac. Students will learn what type of information can be found in each of these reference books.

Lesson 1 • Dictionaries

Give each student a copy of the same dictionary and have each of them look up the word "run." Using "run" as an example, point out the information the dictionary gives:

1. The spelling of the entry word
2. The pronunciation
3. The part of speech
4. The numbered definitions
5. Other forms of the word, with example sentences

When you discuss the pronunciation, point out the pronunciation key that explains the symbols used. The key is usually reproduced on each page of the dictionary.

Ask the students to look up several words and identify the five elements listed above. Be sure to point out that the library contains specialized dictionaries as well—biographical dictionaries, foreign language dictionaries, geographical dictionaries, musical dictionaries, and others. When the students understand how to use the dictionary, hand out the "What Does It Mean?" worksheet (page 46).

Lesson 2 • Atlases

Before class, stack up a pile of atlases from the library. Tell the students that an atlas is a book of maps and charts. Ask them if they can think of times when an atlas would come in handy. Hold up the different kinds of atlases available and point out the charts: rainfall, population, natural resources, and so on.

Show students how to look up their own town in the atlas by using the index. After demonstrating how to find specific maps and cities, ask the students, "Why might a library have to purchase a new atlas? Can you think of something that might change on the atlas?" Explain that the *names* of places sometimes change. For example, some African countries changed their names when they won their independence. Also, when countries change their boundaries after a war, the atlases must reflect these changes.

On the chalkboard, write down the words that are needed to complete the "Atlas Crossword Puzzle" (page 47). Before handing out the crossword puzzle, explain any of the words the students may not know (precipitation, elevation, and so on). The puzzle introduces important words students can use in understanding atlases.

Lesson 3 • Almanacs

Tell the students that the almanac is a reference book published every year. Unlike the information in the encyclopedia, the information in the almanac is always current. If students want to find out who won last year's Super Bowl, for example, they would look in the almanac.

Like an atlas, an almanac has an extensive index. Show the students how to use the almanac's index. Point out some of the topics covered in the almanac: presidents, countries, academy award winners, entertainers, baseball stars, and so on. Ask the students to come up with a few questions they would like to answer by looking in the almanac. Have three or four students look up the answers in the almanac.

Ask the students who their favorite sports stars or entertainers are. Demonstrate how to look up the birthdays of these people. When the students have answered their questions about the almanac, hand out the "Almanac Facts" worksheet (page 48).

Lesson 4 • Reference Test

Review all the information covered in this unit. Talk with the students about the types of information found in each reference book. When the students can distinguish between the kinds of information in each book, hand out the "Reference Test" (page 49).

The Library Skills Test

The "Library Skills Test" (pages 50-55) tests students' understanding of the material presented in all the previous units. Before giving the test, review all the information covered in the units and give students a chance to ask any questions they have. You may want to present the "Library Skills Award" (page 56) to students who do well on the "Library Skills Test."

Call Number Clues

Next to each call number below, write the section of the library in which the book would be found.

1. F Q _____

2. B S _____

3. F G _____

4. R 185 N _____

5. B T _____

6. F S _____

7. R 017 J _____

8. B L _____

Next to each title and author below, write the call number.

9. *Johnny Tremain* by Esther Forbes (a fiction book) _____

10. *Martin Luther King, Jr.* by Jacqueline Harris (a biography) _____

11. *Across Five Aprils* by Irene Hunt (a fiction book) _____

12. *Island of the Blue Dolphins* by Scott O'Dell (a fiction book) _____

13. *A Wrinkle in Time* by Madeleine L'Engle (a fiction book) _____

14. *Albert Einstein* by Milton Dank (a biography) _____

Looking It Up © 1989   David S. Lake Publishers

Questions for the Call Numbers Game

1. What is the *call number* for a fiction book by Elizabeth Gray?

2. What is the *call number* for a fiction book by Scott O'Dell?

3. If the *top line* of the call number is *R,* what kind of book is it?

4. If the *top line* of the call number is *B,* what kind of book is it?

5. What is *one* of the places a call number can be found?

6. What is the *call number* for a fiction book by Katherine Paterson?

7. The author's last name is indicated by the (*top* or *bottom*) of the call number?

8. The section of the library where the book can be found is indicated by the (*top* or *bottom*) of the call number?

9. What is the *call number* for a biography by Abraham Lincoln?

10. What is the *call number* for a fiction book by Esther Forbes?

11. What is the *call number* for a biography of Anne Frank?

12. A book with a call number *F* over *M* would be found in what section of the library?

13. A book with a call number *R* over *123* would be found in what section of the library?

14. Are reference books *fiction* or *nonfiction?*

Game Board

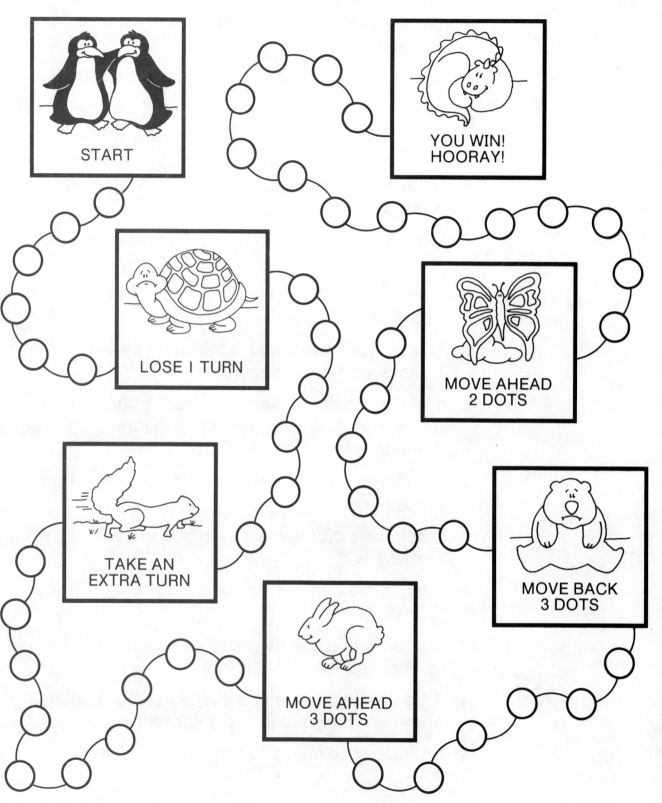

START

YOU WIN! HOORAY!

LOSE I TURN

MOVE AHEAD 2 DOTS

TAKE AN EXTRA TURN

MOVE BACK 3 DOTS

MOVE AHEAD 3 DOTS

Looking It Up © 1989 David S. Lake Publishers

Call Numbers Game Sheet

F O	Catalog Card	F F	Top
Spine	F P	Reference	B L
Book Pocket	F G	Bottom	Book Card
Fiction	B F	Biography	Nonfiction

Looking It Up © 1989 David S. Lake Publishers

Call Numbers Test

Next to each call number below, write the section of the library the book would be found in.

1. B
   L _____   4. F
                                          V _____

2. F
   N _____   5. B
                                          P _____

   R
   123
3. C _____   6. B
                                          T _____

Answer each question below.

7. If you wrote a fiction book, the call number would be _____ .

8. If you wrote the story of your life, the call number would be

   _____ .

9. If you wrote a biography of Abraham Lincoln, the call number would be

   _____ .

10. If you wrote a dictionary, it would be placed in the _____ section of the library.

11. If you wrote a factual book about the life cycle of birds, it would be

    placed in the _____ section of the library.

12. If you wrote a book about the life of a famous doctor, it would be

    placed in the _____ section of the library.

Looking It Up © 1989 David S. Lake Publishers

Next to each title and author, write the call number.

13. *The Girl Who Loved the Wind* by Jane Yolen (a fiction book) _____

14. *Eleanor Roosevelt* by Sharon Whitney (a biography) _____

15. *Marie Curie* by Mollie Keller (a biography) _____

16. *The Witch of Blackbird Pond* by Elizabeth George Spear (a fiction book) _____

17. *Red Planet* by Robert Heinlein (a fiction book) _____

18. *My Side of the Mountain* by Jean George (a fiction book) _____

19. *Margaret Mead* by Jacqueline Ludel (a biography) _____

20. *The Yearling* by Marjorie Rawlings (a fiction book) _____

Library Map Outline

Bookshelves

Questions for the Library Map Game

1. Where would I find a picture book by Bill Martin?
2. Where would I find a book of facts about football?
3. Where would I find a fiction book by Judy Blume?
4. Where would I find a biography of George Washington?
5. Where would I find an encyclopedia?
6. Where would I find a fiction book by Mary Stolz?
7. Where would I find a book of maps?
8. Where would I find a picture book by Dr. Seuss?
9. Where would I find a collection of short stories by Edgar Allan Poe?
10. Where would I find the card catalog?
11. Where would I find a book with an *R* as the top part of the call number?
12. Where would I find a book with a number in the call number?
13. Where would I find a fiction book by Jesse Jackson?
14. Where would I find a dictionary?
15. Where would I find a biography of Alexander Graham Bell?
16. Where would I find a book of facts about snakes?
17. Where would I find a fairy tale collection?
18. Where would I find a collection of short stories by Hoke?
19. Where would I find a magazine?
20. Where would I find a book with an *F* as the top part of the call number?
21. Where would I find a book with a *B* as the top part of the call number?
22. Where would I go to check out a book?
23. Where would I go to find the door out of here?

SUPER STUDENT AWARD

TO _____

FOR _____

_____

_____

_____   _____
TEACHER   DATE

Name _____

Using the Index

Abdomen:
   anatomy of, 13
   pain in, 215, 216
   wounds of, 95
Abrasion, 64
Accidents:
   automobile, 1, 2
   home, 2
   industrial, 2
   prevention of, 2
Acid:
   burns, 183

poisoning, 192, 193
   spills, 183
Alcohol:
   poisoning, 194, 195
   to sterilize, 68
Arm bone fracture, 14
Arteries, 18–22
   bleeding from, 19
   pressure points, 21
Artificial respiration, 109–119
   explanation, 112–119
   technique, 109–112

Asphyxiation, 108–130
   from being buried, 130
   from blows, 130
   from choking, 129
   from drowning, 126–129
   from electric shock, 119–121
   from gas poisoning, 124–126
   from hanging, 120
Automobile:
   accidents, 1, 2
   transporting injured, 222
Back, broken, 163–165

Answer the following questions about the index above.

1. Read the headings. What do you think this book is about? _____

   _____

2. If you had a pain in your abdomen, what pages would you turn to for

   help? _____

3. If you had a broken back, what pages would you turn to? _____

4. In what order are the words in the index listed? _____

5. If you fractured your arm bone, what page would you turn to for

   help? _____

6. If you had an acid burn, what page would you turn to? _____

7. Would this index be in the *front* or the *back* of the book? _____

8. If you had an abrasion, what page would you turn to? _____

9. If you wanted to find out how to prevent accidents, what page would you

   turn to? _____

Looking It Up © 1989 David S. Lake Publishers

Using the Table of Contents

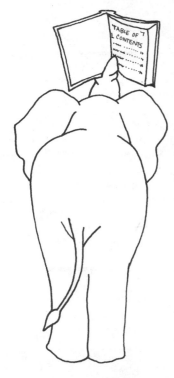

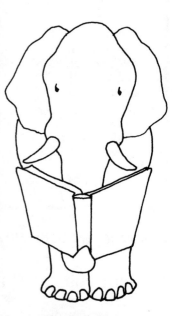

Contents

Use the table of contents above to answer the following questions.

1. Read the chapter titles. What is the main subject of this book?

   _____

2. On what page does the chapter on broken bones begin? _____

3. On what page does the chapter on poisoning begin? _____

4. On what page does the chapter on burns begin? _____

5. On what page is the index? _____

6. Is the table of contents in the *front* or *back* of the book? _____

7. Are the chapters listed in numerical or alphabetical order? _____

8. If you wanted to find out about your blood system, what page would you

   turn to? _____

Looking It Up © 1989   David S. Lake Publishers

Parts-of-a-Book Crossword Puzzle

Read each clue below and print the answer in the puzzle.

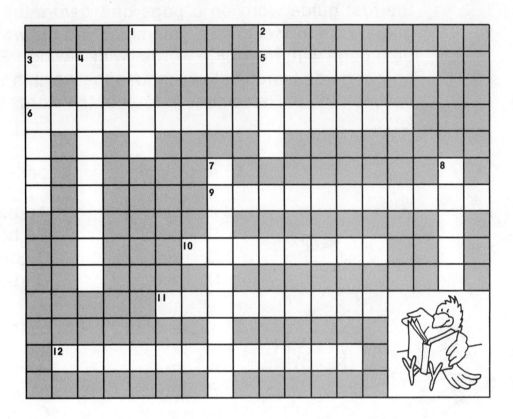

ACROSS

3. Supplementary information in the back of the book (maps, charts, etc.).

5. Note from the author to the reader.

6. List of chapters and their page numbers.

9. Person who drew the pictures.

10. Dictionary of words in the back of the book.

11. Tells you that you may not copy from the book.

12. A list of books on one subject.

DOWN

1. Alphabetical list of subjects and their page numbers.

2. Part of the book you see when you look on a bookshelf.

3. Person who wrote the book.

4. Company that issued the book.

7. Page that gives the title, author, and publisher.

8. The outside of the book that protects the pages.

Gliding Through Guide Words

When you look up a word in the dictionary, the word you are trying to find must come in alphabetical order *after* the first guide word on a page and *before* the second guide word. For example, you might find the word "win" on a page with the guide words "wick—wing." For each pair of guide words below, choose the word that comes between them. Remember to look at the words letter by letter.

1. rage—rain

   A. rake
   B. radio
   C. raid
   D. race

2. shoe—short

   A. shot
   B. shove
   C. shock
   D. shop

3. cane—care

   A. cat
   B. cape
   C. cast
   D. cart

4. ball—bank

   A. banner
   B. bake
   C. bald
   D. band

5. slide—slip

   A. slim
   B. slid
   C. slipper
   D. slit

6. fun—future

   A. full
   B. fuzzy
   C. fur
   D. finish

Looking It Up © 1989 David S. Lake Publishers

Alphabet Scramble

Circle the word in each pair below that would come first in the encyclopedia.

1. Algebra *or* Algeria

2. Annapurna *or* Annapolis

3. Hologram *or* Holstein

4. Industrial Revolution *or* Industrial Relations

5. Dinosaur *or* Diogenes

Circle the name in each pair below that would come first in the encyclopedia.

6. Dr. Seuss *or* Georges Seurat

7. Patrick Henry *or* Matthew Alexander Henson

8. Duke Ellington *or* William Ellery

9. Eleanor Roosevelt *or* Stuart Allen Roosa

10. Pete Seeger *or* Alexander Selkirk

If the last names are the same, the first names are used to determine alphabetical order. Circle the name in each pair below that would come first in the encyclopedia.

11. George Washington *or* Martha Custis Washington

12. Mary Lincoln *or* Abraham Lincoln

13. Jethro Wood *or* Robert Williams Wood

14. Bessie Smith *or* Adam Smith

15. Eleanor Roosevelt *or* Theodore Roosevelt

Looking It Up © 1989 David S. Lake Publishers

The Dewey Decimal System

000—099   General Works
                (encyclopedias, references)

100—199   Philosophy
                (ideas about behavior, thought, and psychology)

200—299   Religion
                (all religions of all times)

300—399   Social Sciences
                (education, law, government, customs)

400—499   Language
                (dictionaries, grammar)

500—599   Pure Science
                (biology, chemistry, physics)

600—699   Technology
                (medicine, industry, agriculture, machinery)

700—799   Arts
                (music, painting, sculpture, games)

800—899   Literature
                (poetry, plays, books about literature)

900—999   History
                (history of civilizations, geography)

Melvil Who?

What do you know about Melvil Dewey? Fill in the blanks below.

1. Melvil Dewey worked in a library where the books were put on the shelves in _____ order by the _____ name.

2. He decided to change the system, so he made up a system that arranged books on the shelf by _____ rather than _____ .

3. His system of putting books on the shelves is called the _____ _____ _____ .

4. If the top line of a call number is a number, it is called a _____ _____ number.

5. If the top line of a call number is a number, the book is a _____ book.

6. Melvil Dewey left the _____ books as he found them.

7. Melvil Dewey's numbering system, or one similar to it, is used in libraries around the world.

   (Circle one.)   True   False

What's the Number?

Dewey Decimal System

000–099 General Works (encyclopedias, reference books)
100–199 Philosophy (ideas about behavior, thought, and psychology)
200–299 Religion (all religions of all times)
300–399 Social Studies (education, law, government, customs, holidays, fairy tales)
400–499 Language (language dictionaries, grammar, language books)
500–599 Pure Science (biology, chemistry, physics, space, wild animals, weather)
600–699 Technology (tools, medicine, agriculture, cooking, sewing, pets)
700–799 Arts (music, painting, sculpture, games, sports, magic tricks)
800–899 Literature (poetry, plays, books about literature)
900–999 History (history of civilizations, geography)

Using the Dewey Decimal System description above, match each book title below with the category it belongs in. Write the Dewey Decimal System numbers in the blanks.

1. *Lions in the Wild*　　　　　_____

2. *Learn How to Draw*　　　　_____

3. *Exploring Space*　　　　　_____

4. *Understanding Chemistry*　_____

5. *Let's Learn French*　　　　_____

6. *Cooking Made Easy*　　　　_____

7. *The Poetry of Robert Frost*　_____

8. *Magic in Your Pocket*　　　_____

9. *Vegetable Farming*　　　　_____

10. *Holidays Around the World*　_____

Looking It Up © 1989 David S. Lake Publishers

11. *The Complete Plays of William Shakespeare* _____

12. *Tornadoes* _____

13. *Buddhism, the Ancient Religion* _____

14. *The Pilgrims in America* _____

15. *The History of Brazil* _____

16. *Philosophy of Man and the Universe* _____

17. *The Music of Bach* _____

18. *Tools for Gardening* _____

19. *Geography of Europe* _____

20. *Bible Stories* _____

21. *The Government of the United States* _____

Cat on a Log 1

Answer the questions about the catalog card shown below.

```
F
C              Cleary, Beverly
                 Ramona Quimby, Age 8
               ill. by Alan Tiegreen
               Morrow, 1981; 190 p.
                 The further adventures of the
               Quimby family as Ramona enters
               the third grade.
               0-688-00478-4


                         ◯
```

1. Is this a *title, author,* or *subject* card? Circle the answer.

2. Who is the author of the book? _____

3. What is the title of the book? _____

4. Who is the publisher of the book? _____

5. Who is the illustrator of the book? _____

6. What is the call number of the book? _____

7. In what section of the library would the book be found?

_____

8. How many pages are in the book? _____

9. Is this a nonfiction book or a fiction book? _____

10. In what year was the book published? _____

Looking It Up © 1989 David S. Lake Publishers

Cat on a Log 2

Answer the questions about the catalog card shown below.

```
F
C              FAMILY LIFE--FICTION

                  Cleary, Beverly
               Ramona Quimby, Age 8
               ill. by Alan Tiegreen
               Morrow, 1981; 190 p.
                  The further adventures of the
               Quimby family as Ramona enters
               the third grade.
               0-688-00478-4
```

1. Is this a *title, author,* or *subject* card? Circle the answer.

2. Who is the author of the book? _____

3. What is the title of the book? _____

4. Who is the publisher of the book? _____

5. Who is the illustrator of the book? _____

6. What is the call number of the book? _____

7. In what section of the library would the book be found?

_____

8. How many pages are in the book? _____

9. Is this a nonfiction book or a fiction book? _____

10. In what year was the book published? _____

Looking It Up © 1989 David S. Lake Publishers

Cat on a Log 3

Answer the questions about the catalog card shown below.

```
F
C                    Ramona Quimby, Age 8

                        Cleary, Beverly
                     Ramona Quimby, Age 8
                     ill. by Alan Tiegreen
                     Morrow, 1981; 190 p.
                        The further adventures of the
                     Quimby family as Ramona enters
                     the third grade.
                     0-688-00478-4
```

1. Is this a *title, author,* or *subject* card? Circle the answer.

2. Who is the author of the book? _____

3. What is the title of the book? _____

4. Who is the publisher of the book? _____

5. Who is the illustrator of the book? _____

6. What is the call number of the book? _____

7. In what section of the library would the book be found?

_____

8. How many pages are in the book? _____

9. Is this a nonfiction book or a fiction book? _____

10. In what year was the book published? _____

Looking It Up © 1989 David S. Lake Publishers

Who Are You?

Look up the book titles below in the card catalog. Write the last name of the author in the blank spaces, one letter per space. When you finish, write the circled letters in the spaces at the bottom of the page to learn the puzzle's answer.

1. Who wrote *Little Women*? ○̲ ___ ___ ___ ___ ___

2. Who wrote *It's A Mystery, Charlie Brown*?
   ○̲ ___ ___ ___ ___ ___

3. Who wrote *Freckle Juice*? ___ ___ ○̲ ___ ___

4. Who wrote *Granny and the Indians*? ○̲ ___ ___ ___ ___

5. Who wrote *Charlotte's Web*? ___ ___ ___ ○̲ ___

6. Who wrote *Ramona Quimby, Age 8*? ___ ___ ___ ___ ○̲ ___

7. Who wrote *The Secret of Terror Castle*? ___ ___ ___ ___ ○̲

8. Who wrote *Little House on the Prairie*? ___ ___ ___ ___ ○̲ ___

9. Who wrote *Draw Fifty Dinosaurs*? ○̲ ___ ___ ___

10. Who wrote *Petunia*? ○̲ ___ ___ ___ ___ ___

11. Who wrote *Eli*? ___ ○̲ ___ ___

12. Who wrote *Curious George*? ○̲ ___ ___

Question: Who are you?   Answer:

___ ___ ___ ___ ___ ___ ___ ___ ___ ___ ___ ___!
1   2   3   4   5   6   7   8   9   10   11   12

Looking It Up © 1989 David S. Lake Publishers

What Am I?

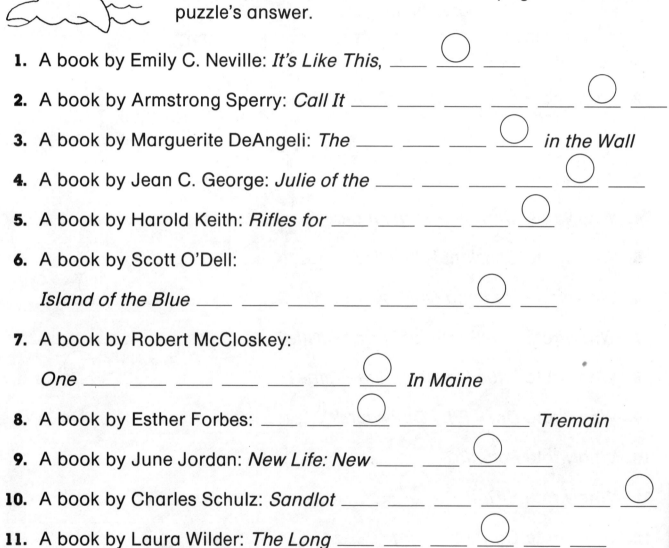

Look up the the authors below in the card catalog. Complete the titles in the blank spaces, writing one letter in each space. When you finish, write the circled letters in the spaces at the bottom of the page to learn the puzzle's answer.

1. A book by Emily C. Neville: *It's Like This,* ___ ◯ ___

2. A book by Armstrong Sperry: *Call It* ___ ___ ___ ___ ◯

3. A book by Marguerite DeAngeli: *The* ___ ___ ___ ◯ *in the Wall*

4. A book by Jean C. George: *Julie of the* ___ ___ ___ ___ ◯ ___

5. A book by Harold Keith: *Rifles for* ___ ___ ___ ___ ◯ ___

6. A book by Scott O'Dell:

    Island of the Blue ___ ___ ___ ___ ___ ___ ◯ ___

7. A book by Robert McCloskey:

    One ___ ___ ___ ___ ___ ___ ◯ *In Maine*

8. A book by Esther Forbes: ___ ___ ◯ ___ ___ ___ *Tremain*

9. A book by June Jordan: *New Life: New* ___ ___ ◯ ___

10. A book by Charles Schulz: *Sandlot* ___ ___ ___ ___ ___ ___ ◯

11. A book by Laura Wilder: *The Long* ___ ___ ___ ◯ ___ ___

Question: What am I?   Answer:

___ ___ ___ ___ ___ ___ ___ ___ ___ ___ ___!
 1   2   3   4   5   6   7   8   9   10 11

Looking It Up © 1989 David S. Lake Publishers

So Many Ways to Paraphrase!

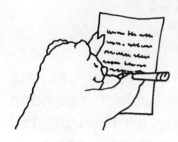

Find an article in the encyclopedia that interests you and read it carefully. When you are done, paraphrase the article (tell about it in your own words) by answering the following questions. *Don't* copy from the article.

1. What was the subject of the article? _____

_____

2. What did you find interesting in the article? _____

_____

_____

_____

_____

_____

3. What did you learn by reading the article? _____

_____

_____

_____

_____

_____

_____

Encyclopedia Wizard

When you look up information in the encyclopedia, you need to know the *key words* of your subject. For each question below, underline the key word or words that you would use to look up the answer to the question.

1. How large is Northern Ireland?

2. When did space travel begin?

3. What does the body's nervous system do?

4. What is the difference between the Greek sphinx and the Egyptian sphinx?

5. Where does a platypus live?

6. When did the Gold Rush begin in California?

7. Why do stars twinkle?

8. What is the moon made of?

9. What is the name of the flying horse of Greek mythology?

10. What do penguins eat?

Choose one of the questions above and look up the answer in an encyclopedia. Write down the number of the question and the answer below.

_____

_____

_____

_____

_____

Looking It Up © 1989 David S. Lake Publishers

Index Clues

Here is part of a typical encyclopedia index.

Indian, American I:302 *with pictures*
    American Indian Movement A:111
    Canada (Ancestry) C:58
    Fur Trade F:541
    Latin America (The People) L:24
    Mission Life in America M:216 *with pictures*
    National Congress of American Indians N:955
    Rocky Mountain States (The People) R:216
    Segregation in the United States S:544
Culture
    Arrowhead A:414
    Beadwork B:312 *with pictures*
    Cliff Dwellers C:312

Using the encyclopedia index entry for "American Indian" above, answer the following questions.

1. Where would you look for general information about American Indians?
   Volume _____ Page _____

2. Where would you look for information about the American Indian fur trade? Volume _____ Page _____

3. Where would you look for information about American Indian beadwork?
   Volume _____ Page _____

4. Where would you look for information about American Indians' Canadian ancestry? Volume _____ Page _____

5. Where would you look for information about the National Congress of American Indians? Volume _____ Page _____

Looking It Up © 1989 David S. Lake Publishers

Encyclopedia Test

Part I. Answer the following questions on the lines given.

1. If you wanted to find information about John F. Kennedy in an

   encyclopedia, what volume would you look in? _____

2. Is it legal to copy word for word from an encyclopedia when you are

   writing a report? _____

3. Is it acceptable to use the outline at the end of an article to help organize

   a report? _____

4. Are bibliographies found in encyclopedias? _____

5. What volume would you look in to find information about Indians?

   _____

6. What volume would you look in to find information about how the

   Shoshone Indians made their houses? _____

7. To find out about sharks, what volume would you look in?

   _____

8. If you wanted to find out what to feed a puppy, you would look up "Dog"

   and then read the section under which heading? _____
   A. Kinds of dogs   B. Life Cycle of a Dog   C. Care of Dogs and Puppies

9. If you wanted to know more about airplanes, what volume would you

look in? _____

10. If you wanted to find information about dinosaurs, what volume would

you look in? _____

Part II. Answer the following questions from the encyclopedia volume you have been given.

1. What is the title of the article you have been given? _____

_____

2. Answer the question on the card here. _____

_____

3. Under what large heading did you find the answer? _____

4. Is there a bibliography at the end of the article? If so, list two of the

books from it here. _____

_____

_____

5. Are there related articles mentioned in the article? If so, list two of them

here. _____

_____

_____

Name _____

What Does It Mean?

Here is part of a typical dictionary page.

doctor (dok′tər), **1** a person trained to treat illness and injuries. *Noun. Plural,* doctors. **2** a person who has the highest degree from a university. **3** to treat disease: *My mother doctored me when I had a sore throat. Verb.*

doctrine (dok′trin), something taught by a nation, church, or group; belief. *Noun. Plural,* doctrines.

document (dok′yə mənt), a written or printed statement that gives information or proof of something. *Noun. Plural,* documents.

does (duz), a present tense of **do**: *She does all her work.*

ă hat	ī it	oi oil	ch child	a in about
ā age	ī ice	ou out	ng long	e in taken
ä far	ŏ hot	ù cup	sh she	i in pencil
ĕ let	ō open	ù put	th thin	o in lemon
ē equal	ô order	ü rule	ŦH then	u in circus
ėr term			zh measure	

ə =

dog (dôg), **1** a four-legged, flesh-eating animal kept as a pet and used for hunting or guarding property. *Noun. Plural,* dogs. **2** to follow closely as a dog does. *Verb.* **dogged, dogging.** *The police dogged the man for over a week.*

dogwood (dôg′wùd), **1** a small tree

Look at the entry word *dog* and answer the following questions.

1. After the entry word *dog,* there is a respelling, (dôg). What does this respelling tell you? _____

2. What is the first definition of *dog*? _____

_____

_____

3. Is the first definition of *dog* a noun or a verb? _____

4. Is the second definition of *dog* a noun or a verb? _____

5. What are the two other forms of the word *dog* given in the second definition? _____

6. To figure out how to pronounce (dôg), where on this dictionary page do you look? _____

7. What are the guide words on this dictionary page? _____

Looking It Up © 1989 David S. Lake Publishers

Atlas Crossword Puzzle

Read each clue below and print the answer in the puzzle.

[crossword grid with numbered squares 1-12]

ACROSS

1. In the atlas, countries are shown in different _____ .
3. Rainfall is called _____ .
8. Oceans, rivers, and _____ are blue on a map.
9. _____ is the height of the land above sea level.
10. If you live in a city or a _____ , you'll find its name in the atlas.
11. Direction opposite from North.
12. _____ show where one country ends and another begins.

DOWN

1. Another word for weather.
2. The map's _____ tells you what each map symbol is.
3. Tells you how many people live in an area.
4. Tells you where to find a certain map in the atlas.
5. Direction opposite from West.
6. Direction opposite from East.
7. Direction opposite from South.

Looking It Up © 1989   David S. Lake Publishers

Name _____

Almanac Facts

Here is part of a typical almanac index.

Sugar—		Planets, relation to	299
Calories	122	Rises, sets	292
Imports	120	Semidiameter	293
Production, U.S.	116	Signs and symbols	257
Summer (season)	232	Solar time	259
Sumter, Fort	54	Sunspot	242
Sun, the		Worship, Egypt	799
Diameter	290	**Sun Bowl Games**	258
Earth, distance from	291	**Super Bowl**	845
Eclipses	293	**Superior, Lake**	388

Look at the index above. Write down the page number on which you might find the answer to each of the following questions.

1. How many calories are there in a teaspoon of sugar? _____

2. What happened at Fort Sumter? _____

3. What is the diameter of the sun? _____

4. Who won the Super Bowl in 1987? _____

5. How big is Lake Superior? _____

6. Where are the Sun Bowl Games held? _____

7. How far is the sun from the earth? _____

8. What are the signs and symbols of the sun? _____

9. How much sugar did the United States produce in 1986? _____

Reference Test

For each of the statements below, decide which reference book would be the best source for the information. Place the letter of the book in the blank next to the statement.

A. Dictionary

B. Encyclopedia

C. Atlas

D. Almanac

1. To find out all about lions. _____

2. To find out who is the current president of France. _____

3. To find out how far it is from Charleston to Columbia. _____

4. To find out how to spell "persimmon." _____

5. To find out the year John F. Kennedy was born. _____

6. To find out who won the Super Bowl last year. _____

7. To find out which movie won the Academy Award last year. _____

8. To find out what "prestidigitator" means. _____

9. To find out all about trees. _____

10. To find out how far it is from Paris to London. _____

11. To find out who is the current governor of New York. _____

12. To find out how to pronounce the word "Saluki." _____

Name

Library Skills Test

Answer each question below.

1. How many books can you check out of the library at one time?

   _____

2. How long can you keep the books you have checked out?

   _____

3. To find a book of facts about animals, you would look in the

   _____ section of the library.

4. To find an encyclopedia or an almanac, you would look in the

   _____ section of the library.

5. To find a novel, you would look in the _____ section of the library.

6. The call number is found on the _____ of the book.

7. Put these words in alphabetical order below:
   Bat, Basket, Ball, Back, Baby

   _____

   _____

   _____

   _____

   _____

Looking It Up © 1989 David S. Lake Publishers

8. Which one of these words would be found on a page with the guide words Car—Comb? Circle the correct word.

Cup   Cow   Cab   Cat   Cone

9. A book with the call number $\frac{F}{R}$ would be in the _____ section of the library.

10. A book with the call number $\frac{123}{M}$ would be in the _____ section of the library.

11. The outside of the book is called the _____ .

12. The part of the book that faces you when you look on the shelf is called

the _____ .

13. The name of the book is called the _____ .

14. The person who wrote the book is called the _____ .

15. The person who drew the pictures is called the _____ .

16. The company that issued the book is called the _____ .

17. The _____ page in the front of the book gives the title, the author, and the publisher.

18. The list of chapters and their page numbers is called the

_____ .

19. An alphabetical list of subjects and their page numbers found in the

back of a book or in a separate volume is called the _____ .

20. A list of books on a certain subject is called a _____ .

21. The three kinds of cards in the card catalog are _____ ,

_____ , and _____ .

22. The cards in the card catalog are in _____ order.

23.

```
E
S        Seuss, Dr.
           The Cat in the Hat
         ill. by Dr. Seuss
         Random House, 1957
           0-394-80001-X


              ◯
```

This is a _____ card.

24.

```
E
S        The Cat in the Hat

           Seuss, Dr.
         The Cat in the Hat
         ill. by Dr. Seuss
         Random House, 1957
           0-394-80001-X

              ◯
```

This is a _____ card.

25.

```
E
S        CATS--FICTION

           Seuss, Dr.
         The Cat in the Hat
         ill. by Dr. Seuss
         Random House, 1957
           0-394-80001-X
              ◯
```

This is a _____ card.

26. The topics in an encyclopedia are in _____ order.

27. An atlas is a book of _____ .

28. To find something in an atlas, you must first look in the _____ .

Looking It Up © 1989 David S. Lake Publishers

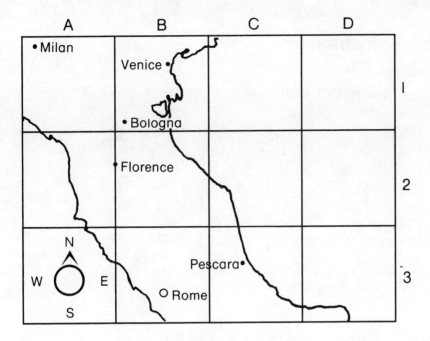

29. On the map above, what city is in B,3? _____

30. Is the city of Florence *North, South, East,* or *West* of Bologna? Circle the correct direction.

31. To find out who won the Super Bowl, you would look in the

_____ .

32. The numbers on the nonfiction section books are arranged according to

what system? _____

33. Put these books in proper library order.

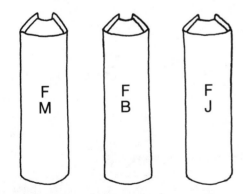

Correct call number order: ____ ____ ____

34. Put these books in proper library order.

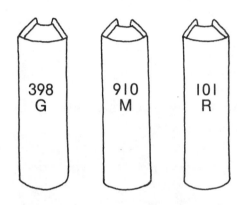

Correct call number order: _____ _____ _____

35. Put these books in proper library order.

Correct call number order: _____ _____ _____

36. To find out how to spell a word, you would look in the

_____ .

37. To find out all about cats, you would look in the _____ .

38. To find out how far it is from San Francisco to Charleston, you would

look in the _____ .

39. To find out who the president of France is now, you would look in the

_____ .

40. Melvil Dewey created the _____ .

41. If you wanted to look for books on the subject of fishing, you would look

in the _____ .

Looking It Up © 1989 David S. Lake Publishers

42. To find out what time the sun will rise on your birthday this year, you would look in the _____ .

43. To find a book about the life of a famous scientist, you would look in the _____ section of the library.

44. To find a fiction book by Judy Blume, you would look for the call number _____ .

45. To find out the origin of the word "epicure," you would look in the _____ .

LIBRARY SKILLS AWARD

TO _____

FOR _____

_____

_____
TEACHER   DATE

Looking It Up © 1989   David S. Lake Publishers

Answer Key

Call Number Clues, page 18
1. Fiction
2. Biography
3. Fiction
4. Reference
5. Biography
6. Fiction
7. Reference
8. Biography
   F
9. F
   B
10. K
   F
11. H
   F
12. O
   F
13. L
   B
14. E

Questions for Call Numbers Game, page 19
   F
1. G
   F
2. O
3. Reference
4. Biography
5. Spine, Book Card, Book Pocket, or Catalog Card
   F
6. P
7. Bottom
8. Top
   B
9. L
   F
10. F
   B
11. F
12. Fiction
13. Reference
14. Nonfiction

Call Numbers Test, page 22
1. Biography
2. Fiction
3. Reference
4. Fiction
5. Biography
6. Biography
7. Answers will vary.
8. Answers will vary.
   B
9. L
10. Reference
11. Nonfiction
12. Biography
   F
13. Y
   B
14. R
   B
15. C
   F
16. S
   F
17. H
   F
18. G
   B
19. M
   F
20. R

Using the Index, page 27
1. First aid
2. 215, 216
3. 163–165
4. Alphabetical
5. 14
6. 183
7. Back
8. 64
9. 2

Using the Table of Contents, page 28

1. First aid
2. 131
3. 192
4. 180
5. 223
6. Front
7. Numerical
8. 18

Parts-of-a-Book Crossword Puzzle, page 29

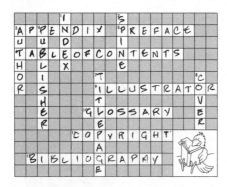

Gliding Through Guide Words, page 30

1. raid
2. shop
3. cape
4. band
5. slim
6. fur

Alphabet Scramble, page 31

1. Algebra
2. Annapolis
3. Hologram
4. Industrial Relations
5. Dinosaur
6. Georges Seurat
7. Patrick Henry
8. William Ellery
9. Stuart Allen Roosa
10. Pete Seeger
11. George Washington
12. Abraham Lincoln
13. Jethro Wood
14. Adam Smith
15. Eleanor Roosevelt

Melvil Who? page 33

1. alphabetical, author's
2. subject, author
3. Dewey Decimal System
4. Dewey Decimal
5. nonfiction
6. fiction
7. True

What's the Number? page 34

1. 500–599
2. 700–799
3. 500–599
4. 500–599
5. 400–499
6. 600–699
7. 800–899
8. 700–799
9. 600–699
10. 300–399
11. 800–899
12. 500–599
13. 200–299
14. 900–999
15. 900–999
16. 100–199
17. 700–799
18. 600–699
19. 900–999
20. 200–299
21. 300–399

Cat on a Log 1-3, pages 36-38

1. Author (1); Subject (2); Title (3)
2. Beverly Cleary
3. *Ramona Quimby, Age 8*
4. Morrow
5. Alan Tiegreen
6. F over C
7. Fiction
8. 190
9. Fiction
10. 1981

Who Are You? page 39

1. Alcott
2. Schulz
3. Blume
4. Parish
5. White
6. Cleary
7. Arthur
8. Wilder
9. Ames
10. Duvoisin
11. Peet
12. Rey
Answer: A Super Reader!

What Am I? page 40

1. Cat
2. Courage
3. Door
4. Wolves
5. Watie
6. Dolphins
7. Morning
8. Johnny
9. Room
10. Peanuts
11. Winter
Answer: A Green Ghost!

Encyclopedia Wizard, page 42

1. Northern Ireland (5,452 sq. miles)
2. Space (Oct 4, 1957, launch of Sputnik I)
3. Nervous System (internal communication network helps the body respond to changes in the environment)
4. Sphinx (Greek sphinx usually has the head of a woman; Egyptian sphinx has the head of a man and the body of a lion)
5. Platypus (streams of Australia and Tasmania)
6. Gold Rush (1849; James Wilson Marshall found gold in 1848)
7. Stars (starlight appears to us through moving layers of air that surround the earth)
8. Moon (rock, gravel, and glass)
9. Greek mythology (Pegasus)
10. Penguins (small fish)

Index Clues, page 43

1. I, 302
2. F, 541
3. B, 312
4. C, 58
5. N, 955

Encyclopedia Test, page 44-45
Part I

1. K
2. No
3. Yes
4. Yes
5. I
6. Index
7. S
8. C
9. A
10. D

Part II

1–5. Answers will vary.

What Does It Mean? page 46

1. How to pronounce the word
2. A four-legged, flesh-eating animal kept as a pet and used for hunting or guarding property.
3. Noun
4. Verb
5. Dogged, dogging
6. Upper right (pronunciation key)
7. Doctor/dollar

Atlas Crossword Puzzle, page 47

Almanac Facts, page 48

1. 122
2. 54
3. 290
4. 845
5. 388
6. 258
7. 291
8. 257
9. 116

Reference Test, page 49

1. B
2. D
3. C
4. A
5. B or D
6. D
7. D
8. A
9. B
10. C
11. D
12. A

Library Skills Test, pages 50-55

1-2. Answers will vary
3. nonfiction
4. reference
5. fiction
6. spine
7. Baby
   Back
   Ball
   Basket
   Bat
8. Cat
9. fiction
10. nonfiction
11. cover
12. spine
13. title
14. author
15. illustrator
16. publisher
17. title
18. table of contents
19. index
20. bibliography
21. title, author, subject
22. alphabetical
23. author
24. title
25. subject
26. alphabetical
27. maps
28. index
29. Rome
30. South
31. almanac
32. Dewey Decimal System
    F F F
33. B J M
    B B B
34. B S Y
    101 398 910
35. R   G   M
36. dictionary
37. encyclopedia
38. atlas
39. almanac
40. Dewey Decimal System
41. card catalog
42. almanac
43. biography
    F
44. B
45. dictionary